Contents

Published By Century Books Limted,
Unit I, Upside Station Building,
Solsbro Road, Torquay, Devon, TQ2 6FD.
books@centurybooksltd.co.uk Published 2012.

Under license from Bravado Merchandising.
All rights reserved.

Check out the official store at
www.thesaturdays.co.uk

THE SATURDAYS

It's hard to believe that the five of us are here already, looking at the pages of our official 2013 Saturdays Annual! It has been another amazing year, made extra-magical of course by you, our fans. This book is our way of saying thank you. As you flick through, hopefully you'll learn some stuff about us and have fun along the way, too. Go Team Sats!

Lots of love,

£7.99

A Year to Remember

Sooooo much has happened since the band's last annual! As well as two very special weddings and a gorgeous new addition to The Saturdays' family, there have been tons of awesome vids, shows and gigs. The girls are ready to share their fave memories from the last 12 months…

"We've had an incredible year – so much has happened it's hard to pick out just one thing. Travelling is always fun and this year I've really loved the tour and all the trips abroad. Rochelle and I also represented the band when we went out to Africa for Comic Relief which was a privilege but also a real eye-opener."

"This year has been really exciting because we're finally getting the chance to do some work over in the United States. We've been out there on several trips for meetings already this year and it now looks like we're going over there for a big chunk of time to work on a new project. Pulling that off has been very exciting."

"Our video shoots were memorable this year, for totally different reasons. When we shot 'My Heart Takes Over' in Iceland we nearly got blown off some cliffs – it was freezing but completely worth it.

For '30 Days' it was funny to be surrounded by so many guys and watch Mollie chatting with them all. I used to be labelled the band flirt, but recently I've handed the flirting baton to Mollie!"

"I've loved branching out and writing my blog for InStyle. Every month I get to write a diary and upload pictures of what I've been up to.

Rochelle and I also had lots of fun when we did a front cover shoot for Cosmopolitan magazine. It was fun to do something with just the two of us – although it felt a bit weird (and quiet!) at first."

"I loved the 'All Fired Up' Tour. It was always going to be special. We felt we had really come such a long way to be able to headline our own arena dates. I've got a gorgeous photo of us on stage at Wembley, standing there, taking everything in. It's so amazing I've had it framed."

Spotlight On Rochelle

She's the 'big sister' Saturday who looks after the rest of the girls and is a knockout performer to boot! We love Rochelle's modesty, bubbly chatter and dazzling smile.

Full name:	Rochelle Eulah Eileen Wiseman
Date of birth:	21st March 1989
Born:	Barking, East London
Pets:	Yorkshire terrier, Tiger
Hobbies:	Paragliding, cooking, cracking super-tough jigsaw puzzles
Fave saying:	"Oh, wow"
Fave film:	*Pretty Woman*

"I love every minute of this job! I think I'm the luckiest person in the world."

Did you know...?

She and JLS hottie Marvin Humes are blissfully happy newlyweds.

Rochelle used to have an African land snail as a pet (for real!).

Footie manager and ex-England star Paul Ince is Rochelle's uncle.

Top time out

"I do like to walk Tiger, my dog. She's very happy, although she's definitely got 'only child' syndrome! She's great around children but if another dog sits on my lap she gets jealous. Unfortunately Tiger wasn't at the wedding. I did toy with the idea of her coming along as a ring-bearer, but she's so tiny I was worried someone would step on her or she'd eat the rings and we'd have to wait for her to poo them out!"

Twitter talk

Follow @RochelleTheSats

Spotlight On Mollie

Mollie has got to be the chirpiest Saturday, a sunny-natured girl that sees the good in everything. The rest of the group love her upbeat attitude so much they even call her 'Miss Disney'!

Full name:	Mollie Elizabeth King
Date of birth:	4th June 1987
Born:	Richmond, Surrey
Pets:	Alfie the poodle
Hobbies:	Jet skiing, water-skiing, basically anything on water!
Fave saying:	"Check this bad boy out!"
Fave artist:	Britney Spears (she's been to every tour!)

"Meeting our fans is one of the nicest parts of the job."

Did you know…?

Her idol is Carrie Bradshaw, SJP's fashionista from Sex And The City.

Mollie auditioned for The X Factor in 2005, before entering again in 2007 as part of a girl group called Fallen Angelz.

She's got a phobia of itty, bitty things like Jelly Tots and Skittles!

Top time out

"Even on days off we try and get together – I live close to Frankie so I see her or I meet the other girls in town. I have my dog Alfie, so I enjoy taking him on walks or meeting up with my parents and going out for breakfast."

Twitter talk

Follow @MollieTheSats

Spotlight On Frankie

With her awesome hair, effortless style and up-front attitude – all eyes are on Frankie! Una describes Frankie as the group's 'tactile, flirtatious Saturday', but she's honest and generous too, giving up lots of time to help the charities she cares about.

Full name:	Francesca Sandford
Date of birth:	14th January 1989
Born:	Upminster, London
Pets:	Pug Presley and Chihuahua Pixie
Hobbies:	Camping and outdoorsy stuff
Fave saying	"Awesome!"
Fave TV show:	*One Tree Hill*

"Being on stage and doing my thing is just amazing."

Did you know…?

Frankie dreams of working with Rihanna one day.

She's crazy about her dogs Presley and Pixie – the pups even have their own Twitter accounts!

Frankie is going out with footballer Wayne Bridge.

Top time out

"Wayne and I love to just hang out. We have a major obsession with chicken fajitas so we stay in and eat them. I don't really enjoy football but I'm more into it since being with Wayne. I like going to watch him play sometimes. Luckily he's not a guy that wants to permanently have footie on the TV. We watched a few matches for the Euros together, but I've already forgotten which ones!"

Twitter talk

Follow @FrankieTheSats

Spotlight On Una

2012 has been an unforgettable year for Una – as well as having an adorable new baby, she had a magical *Midsummer Night's Dream* themed wedding. The other Sats say that Una can sometimes be a party animal with an irresistible naughty streak!

Name:	Una Theresa Imogene Healy
Date of birth:	10th October 1981
Born:	Thurles, Republic of Ireland
Pet:	Cats, terrapins, plus dogs Jackson and Bono
Hobbies:	Going to the movies
Fave saying:	"You know what I mean, like!"
Fave memory:	Auditioning for the Sats

"Life in the Saturdays is like a rollercoaster!"

Did you know…?

Una was an all-Ireland swimming champion by the age of nine.

She has a family recipe for brown soda bread that is said to be de-lish!

She and her husband Ben Foden have beautiful baby girl called Aoife Belle.

Top time out

"I mostly spend my free time with Ben and Aoife, but I do get to go out every now and then. We recently went to our A&R person's engagement party and of course Rochelle and I had a joint hen do. We don't go out partying in London together that much though. When we're not working, we all like to relax."

Twitter talk

Follow @UnaTheSats

Spotlight On Vanessa

Although Vanessa is the baby of the band, she's not afraid to take the lead sometimes. The Sats can't resist their friend's cheeky humour and infectious giggles!

Full name:	Vanessa Karen White
Date of birth:	30th October 1989
Born:	Yeovil, Somerset
Pets:	3 Dogs; George, Peaches and Maggie the Puggle (that's half pug and half beagle!)
Hobbies:	Vanessa loves getting away from it all on her hols. She wants to go surfing in Hawaii next.
Fave saying:	"Oh stop it!"
Fave vacation:	The Philippines

"I love writing songs. I write them on my own in my bedroom."

Did you know…?

Whether it's an eighties night or a Hawaiian hula, Vanessa can't resist a themed party.

She comes from the same neighbourhood as Jade from the Sugababes.

Vanessa is not a morning person. If you want to ask her something – wait til after midday!

Top time out

"I love going to festivals. My boyfriend and I recently went to Wireless both days in a row. On the Saturday we met up with the girls in the VIP area – the JLS boys were also there. On the second day I wanted to do it like everyone else, so we just went in with the crowd. I had no idea how muddy it was going to be! Afterwards I had to throw the Creeper boots I'd been wearing away as they were wrecked. It was a brilliant laugh though. I loved watching Drake, Nicki Minaj and Rihanna."

Twitter talk

Follow @VanessaTheSats

Are you ready to push your Saturdays knowledge to the limit? The girls have put together a five-part SATS quiz to find out if you have what it takes to call yourself a true fan. When you've completed all five tests, check your answers on Page 92 and total up your score.

Start by ticking the correct answers to complete the following 15 statements. Simple right?! Let's see…

1. The only member of The Saturdays to have auditioned for The X Factor is…
- [ ] Frankie
- [ ] Vanessa
- [ ] Mollie

2. The band were formed in…
- [ ] 2006
- [ ] 2007
- [ ] 2008

3. The members of the band who enjoyed early success with an act called S Club 8 were Frankie and…
- [ ] Rochelle
- [ ] Una
- [ ] Vanessa

4. At the age of 9, Una was an All-Ireland Champion…
- [ ] runner
- [ ] swimmer
- [ ] javelin thrower

5. The youngest member of The Saturdays is…
- [ ] Frankie
- [ ] Vanessa
- [ ] Mollie

6. The girls won the accolade for 'Best Band' at which 2011 award ceremony…
- [ ] The Brits
- [ ] Glamour Awards
- [ ] MTV Europe Music Awards

7. The stars had a documentary on ITV2 called…
- [ ] The Saturdays: 24/7
- [ ] The Saturdays: Uncut
- [ ] The Saturdays: Access All Areas

8. In July 2008, the band released their first single. It was called…

☐ 'If This Is Love'
☐ 'Up'
☐ 'Issues'

9. Una welcomed a new member to The Saturdays' family in March 2012, a baby daughter named…

☐ Niamh
☐ Clodagh
☐ Aoife

10. Mollie's middle name is…

☐ Eleanor
☐ Elizabeth
☐ Erica

11. As well experiencing pop success with the Sats, Rochelle has also dabbled in…

☐ talent show judging
☐ news reading
☐ TV presenting

12. In between Saturdays' albums Vanessa had a brief stint on…

☐ Celebrity Masterchef
☐ Popstar To Opera Star
☐ Dancing On Ice

13. After twice pipping them to the number one spot in the charts, American rapper Flo Rida agreed to…

☐ collaborate with the band
☐ take the band out to dinner
☐ buy 10 copies of their album

14. The song 'Notorious' appears on the album…

☐ 'Wordshaker'
☐ 'Chasing Lights'
☐ 'On Your Radar'

15. The band's first taste of life on tour came when they were booked as the support act for…

☐ McFly
☐ Girls Aloud
☐ JLS

Saturday Girls Crossword

It's time to test your Saturdays credentials once again! Grab a pencil or pen, then work your way through the crossword clues, filling in the spaces on the grid. Can you get the whole puzzle done in less than 15 minutes?

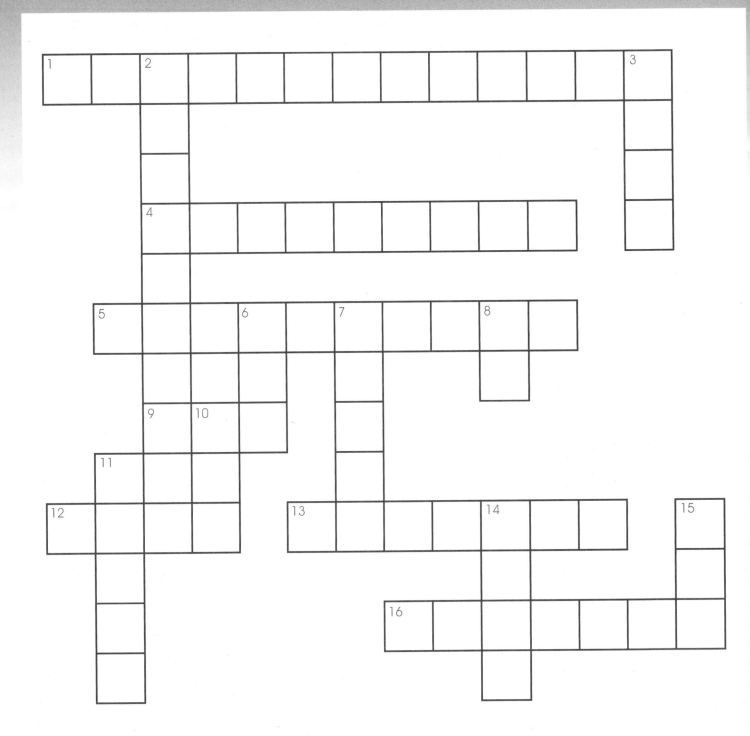

Only serious Sats fans stand a chance – good luck!

Across:

1. The title of the girls' sixth single and a true pop-rock classic. (7, 2, 4)

4. The Band have released 4 albums, but this one was just mini. (9)

5. According to the band, if you feel this way, 'you feel alive'. (3, 5, 2)

9. Self or personality, also the name of the Sats' second-shortest song title. (3)

12. Depeche mode classic reinvented for a new generation, 'Just ___ ' _ Get Enough'. (4)

13. A member of S Club Juniors, along with Rochelle. (7)

16. The group member with the surname White. (7)

Down:

2. The Saturday with strong links to boy band JLS. (8)

3. The last moniker of the rapper who added his flavour to 'Higher'. (4)

6. The first part of the above rapper's name. (3)

7. The Album "On Your _ _ _ _ _" (5)

8. The Sats' shortest ever song title. (2)

10. The third word of the band's fourth single! (3)

11. A brooding ballad, with a video shot in Iceland, 'My Heart _ _ _ _ _ Over'. (5)

14. Mollie's surname. (4)

15. The only Irish member of the band. (3)

Just Can't Get Enough Of...

Rochelle then:

Rochelle says that she started singing and dancing at the age of four… and has never stopped! Along with Frankie, she attended the Collins Performing Arts School in Essex. Things didn't always come easy, and there were often times when Rochelle and her mum had to work part-time jobs in order to pay the school fees. The rising star even taught ballet to help make ends meet.

Rochelle now:

Rochelle is the big sister Saturday who's best friend is her Mum. Although she had to work hard as a child, she doesn't regret a thing. Singing and dancing has always meant everything to her.

On love and relationships:

"Marvin and I have been together three years this November. Time's flown by. We are now married so my surname has changed which has meant I have had to practice my new signature.

My fave new way to spend an evening with Marvin is to pretend that we're on *Strictly Come Dancing*. I don't actually want to go on the programme, but I love giving it a go in the privacy of my own home. I YouTube various dances and we try mastering the lifts! We don't dress up – in fact the other day I was wearing my tiger print onesie. Marvin and I have matching onesies. My sister thought it would be funny to buy the whole family a onesie so that we could all wear them on Christmas Day. Ours have tiger stripes and ears!"

On being all grown up:

"This year we've had so much going on in our professional and our personal lives. I'm doing grown up things, but I still feel very much a kid at heart.

I'd like children one day, but not just yet. Una having Aoife has been amazing. I spoke to her when she was on the way to hospital. When the baby was born, Ben rang me straight away and said 'she's here, but don't tell anyone!' It was really naughty but I couldn't help myself. I was so excited that I rang Vanessa."

Frankie on Rochelle:

"Rochelle is funny, quite loud and confident. She's also a real tidy freak."

Vanessa on Rochelle:

"Rochelle is like the big sister of the band. I always know that she'll look after us."

Mollie on Rochelle:

"If I ever needed any advice or anything, Rochelle would be the one I'd go to."

Frankie on Rochelle:

"We've known each other since we were nine so we kind of have this unsaid bond."

Rochelle

Sats Style: Stage Couture

Whether they're playing their own arena tours, joining other pop bands at a music festival or making a club PA – The Saturdays always look hot! The girls put a lot of effort into getting their onstage style just right. Flick through the Sats' costume rail and find out why the band always stands out from the crowd!

Colour blocking

Frankie is a huge fan of colour blocking, the art of deliberately wearing colours that clash. For the 'All Fired Up' Tour she wowed the crowds with this saucy pink, red and black look!

Fabulous florals

It's not all rock chic, sometimes the Sats like to go girlie! Rochelle perfectly captured the summer vibe during a gig on Clapham Common in 2011. She kept things simple in a cool flower print dress twinned with a tan belt.

Perfect playsuits

The girls often coordinate their look but manage to find ways to each give their own take on the same theme. At T4 On The Beach in 2009 they all chose a short playsuit (a Saturdays staple!) with heels and thick black belt in five fabulous designs.

Glamour puss

Mollie added her own sense of style to this one-of-a-kind rhinestone playsuit. Simple, yet super sparkly and eye-catching, it even comes with a matching microphone!

Festive fun

In the Sats' book, onstage fashion shouldn't be too serious. When they hit the road in December 2011 for the 'All Fired Up Tour', the girls opted for a cheeky Santa's helper look, much to the delight of the crowd!

Accentuate the positive

The girls are experts at showing off their best assets. For an appearance in Tipperary, Ireland in June 2012, the Sats used silver PVC and sequins to accessorise their corset belts.

Vintage re-visited

Vanessa took inspiration from the 1920s for this sparkly flapper outfit in 2011. With feathers, sequins and diamantés attached, this was one dress that didn't need a single accessory!

Una rocks!

Una rocks! Miss Healy went for a grunge look when the girls played the Ultrasound Music Festival in September 2011. Leather trousers, jacket and bustier top are the ultimate rocker's uniform!

Discography

It's incredible to think that the Sats released their first song way back in July 2008! Since then the girls have hardly been out of the top ten. Let's take a peek through their incredible music catalogue…

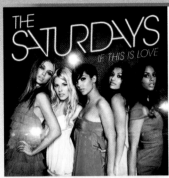

Song title: If This Is Love

Released: 27th July 2008

Chart position: 8

The sound: An electro-pop powerhouse! What a way to say 'hello world!'

Song title: Work

Released: 29th June 2009

Chart position: 22

The sound: The girls show they have hip-hop flavor to burn!

Song title: Up

Released: 12th Oct. 2008

Chart position: 5

The sound: Catchier than a cold, a pure pop stomper!

Song title: Forever Is Over

Released: 4th Oct. 2009

Chart position: 2

The sound: A new pop-rock sound that proved an instant hit with the fans!

Song title: Issues

Released: 4th Jan. 2009

Chart position: 4

The sound: A smooth mid-tempo track, great for sing-alongs!

Song title: Ego

Released: 3rd Jan. 2010

Chart position: 9

The sound: Impossible to get the song out of your head

Song title: Just Can't Get Enough

Released: 1st March 2009

Chart position: 2

The sound: The girls cover Depeche Mode's pop classic for Comic Relief

Song title: Missing You

Released: 5th August 2010

Chart position: 3

The sound: Halfway between a ballad and a dance floor anthem. Go Girls!

Song title: Higher

Released: 31st Oct. 2010

Chart position: 10

The sound: Superstar rapper Flo Rida guests on this infectious fan favourite

Title: Chasing Lights

Released: 27th Oct. 2008

Chart position: 9

Song title: Notorious

Released: 20th May 2011

Chart position: 8

The sound: An edgy and naughty dance floor filler!

Title: Wordshaker

Released: 12th Oct. 2009

Chart position: 9

Song title: All Fired Up

Released: 4th Sept, 2011

Chart position: 3

The sound: Try and sit still for this grown-up club classic!

Title: Headlines [mini-album]

Released: 13th Aug. 2010

Chart position: 3

Song title: My Heart Takes Over

Released: 11th Nov. 2011

Chart position: 15

The sound: A tender love song, don't mess with these girls' hearts!

Song title: 30 Days

Released: 11th May 2012

Chart position: 7

The sound: The girls take their fans to a club for the first taste of their fourth album

Title: On Your Radar

Released: 21st Nov. 2011

Chart position: 23

On Your Radar

The Sats' are known (and loved!) for their amazing style and fresh, fun and funky attitude, but their first passion is the music. Have you sung along to the tunes on the girls' third album, 'On Your Radar'?

'On Your Radar' vital statistics

Released:	21st November 2011
Number of tracks:	12 plus two UK bonus tracks
Songs:	All Fired Up
	Notorious
	Faster
	My Heart Takes Over
	Get Ready, Get Set
	The Way You Watch Me
	For Myself
	Do What You Want With Me
	Promise Me
	Wish I Didn't Know
	White Lies
	Last Call
Bonus tracks:	I Say OK
	Move On U
Singles:	Notorious
	All Fired Up
	My Heart Takes Over

Telling stories

After releasing the mini-album 'Headlines' in 2010, the band were feeling inspired so they started work on a new full-length release straightaway. However, right from the start, they knew that they wanted to try something different.

"We want the whole album to be 'fresh' and have a completely different sound from our previous albums," they admitted. "We don't want to be releasing the same type of music."

"We've all grown up a bit now and that shows," added Vanessa. "It's a lot more R&B and dancey than anything we've done before, it's very cool. Every time I think about 'Notorious' it makes me want to dance."

Helping hands

In order to achieve this new sound, the band worked with some of the coolest, and most in demand producers and artists in the world.

Xenomania:

The hit factory Xenomania have produced and written massive songs for everyone from Girls Aloud and the Sugababes to Kylie Minogue and The Wanted.

Space Cowboy

Lady Gaga's personal DJ and frequent co-writer dropped in to help on 'All Fired Up.'

Ina Wroldsen & Steve Mac

The writers and producers behind some of The Saturdays previous biggest hits, including 'Higher' and 'Ego'. They have been a key part of the Saturdays team from day one.

Travie McCoy:

The lead vocalist of Gym Class Heroes was only too happy to add one of his trademark raps to the album. He collaborated with the girls on the track 'The Way You Watch Me'.

MNEK

Young and talented super producer MNEK, who's also written and produced songs for Tinie Tempah before launching his own solo career.

The sleeve!

Fans of the band were excited about the album before they even heard a note, thanks to its cover art. The girls were keen to show off their vulnerable sides, so the cover features a very simple, yet striking, shot of each of their faces. It was the first time that the group had written a major part of an album (they wrote half of the album's fourteen tracks) so they wanted an image that reflected how 'exposed' they were through their often-personal lyrics. To achieve the photo, the band worked with renowned photographer Elisabeth Hoff.

Did you know?

There are three different versions of the album available. A standard version, the Collector's Edition (one for each member) and the Fan's Edition (with the Headlines Tour DVD).

The first time fans got to hear anything off the album was 20th May 2011, when Radio 1's Chris Moyles played 'Notorious'.

11 studios were used to make the album. One in Sweden, four in the United States and six in the UK.

The band began work on a follow-up to 'On Your Radar' in December 2011. We can't wait to hear it!

Just Can't Get Enough Of...

Mollie then:

Mollie broke the mould when she announced to her surprised parents that she wanted to be a singer! None of the King family had ever expressed an interest in performing and at first they assumed that the youngster would just grow out of it! Kylie was Mollie's first heroine and she spent many hours singing into her hairbrush, mimicking the star. Things got serious when Britney Spears hit the scene. The moment she saw Britney, Mollie knew that she had to follow in her footsteps.

Mollie now:

Mollie is still the smiley, upbeat, hopelessly romantic family girl that used to sing to her hairbrush. And yes, despite all the fame and fortune, she is still Britney's number one fan!

On love and relationships:

"In the past, I've found the idea of getting married quite daunting but seeing Una do it made me think that I'd like to as well one day. I'm single. Being on my own is a shock to the system, but spending time in my own company has helped me get to know myself better. I've also been able to see more of my friends and family."

On being all grown up:

"Although we're older, the five of us are just the same. We still act like excitable 16 year olds!

The Sats had such a lovely day at Una's wedding. We all walked down the aisle, took our seats and burst into tears. Frankie had to wipe my face because OK! magazine was there! Watching Una and Ben say their vows was unforgettable. I'd never been to a best friend's wedding before."

Frankie on Mollie:

"Mollie makes me laugh even when she's not trying to be funny. She's so naive and so sweet."

Vanessa on Mollie

"Mollie is incredible. You never see her moping around. She is permanently upbeat and smiley 24/7. We call her Miss Disney because she's like a Disney character."

Una on Mollie:

"Mollie is a very, very smiley person. She's the kind of girl that every guy wants to take home to his mother."

Rochelle on Mollie:

"She's like an angel. I didn't really know that girls like her existed. She's innocent, although I'm trying to shake that out of her!"

Mollie

Dance Along!

When it comes to performing, the Saturday girls know how to bust some moves! Frankie's favourite stage routine is 'Ego' – She can't resist the classic Ego Move where the girls raise their hand above their head.

Have you got the moves to be the sixth Saturday? Have a go by following the steps to 'Ego' in front of your bedroom mirror. Find a hairbrush to sing into, cue up the track and get dancing! The steps have been written underneath each set of lyrics, but you could also watch the girls online to get the timing just right.

Ego

1. Stand hands on hips

We used to go together
Looking after each other
I thought that you were better
Look at you (look at you, look at you, look at you)

2. Raise alternate shoulders to the beat then lean back to the left

You used to be so laid back

3. Raise alternate shoulders to the beat then pretend to wipe sweat off brow.

You always kept it so cool

4. Walk around in a circle, sashaying hips.

I loved you coz of all that
That's the truth
(that's the truth, that's the truth, that's the truth)

5. Hand to head, then place both hands on hips and dip to the beat like a puppet.

I don't think you know where your head is
I was always there to help you break the fall

6. Hands on hips and flick to the side, then raise both hands up like a star.

And now you wanna pretend that you're a superstar

7. Point to the audience then open both arms wide.

And now you want us to end what's taken you this far

8. Move to the beat with hands on hips.

Don't tell me that you're done as far as we go

9. Do a sitting motion with right hand, then raise it up above your head twice to the words 'ego'.

You need to have a sit down with your ego

10. Move to the beat with hands on hips.

When everyone's gone and you are by yourself
You know that your gonna come to me for help

11. Run both hands up through hair and then point at the audience.

Don't tell me that it's time for going solo

12. Clap on 'sense', then raise hand up above your head twice to the word 'ego'

You need to knock some sense into your ego
(ego, ego, ego) Yeah

13. Stand hands on hips

You act like you're on fire
Living your delusion
You just need you to take you higher
off you go (off you go, off you go) Yeah

14. Hand to head, then place both hands on hips and dip to the beat like a puppet.

You can't make the call when you're ready
I will not be here to help you break the fall

15. Hands on hips and flick to the side, then raise both hands up like a star.

And now you wanna pretend that you're a superstar

16. Point to the audience then open both arms wide.

And now you want us to end what's taken you this far

17. Move to the beat with hands on hips.

Don't tell me that you're done as far as we go

18. Do a sitting motion with right hand, then raise it up above your head twice to the words 'ego'.]

You need to have a sit down with your ego

19. Move to the beat with hands on hips.

When everyone's gone and you are by yourself
You know that your gonna come to me for help

20. Run both hands up through hair and then point at the audience.

Don't tell me that it's time for going solo

21. Clap on 'sense', then raise hand up above your head twice to the word 'ego'.

You need to knock some sense into your ego
(ego, ego, ego) Yeah

22. Freestyle to the beat

And when its time for you to come back down to
where you started, where we parted
I think you'll find that it is very hard to face
reality is a simple thing

23. Hands on hips and flick to the side, then raise both hands up like a star.

And now you wanna pretend that you're a superstar

24. Point to the audience then open both arms wide.

And now you want us to end what's taken you this far

25. Move to the beat with hands on hips.

Don't tell me that you're done as far as we go

26. Do a sitting motion with right hand, then raise it up above your head twice to the words 'ego'.

You need to have a sit down with your ego

27. Move to the beat with hands on hips.

When everyone's gone and you are by yourself
You know that your gonna come to me for help

28. Run both hands up through hair and then point at the audience.

Don't tell me that it's time for going solo
You need to knock some sense into your ego
(ego, ego, ego) Yeah

Putting on an arena tour is a major achievement for any artist – for The Saturdays it was mega! From the day that the run was announced, the girls made it their priority to create a feast for the eyes and ears, combining their killer tunes with flashing lights, dancers and fabulous on-stage fashion.

During the run-up to the tour, Una hit the headlines when she announced that she and her fiancé Ben Foden were expecting a baby. Fans were worried that this would put an end to her appearances, but the mummy-to-be had no intention of stepping down! Even though she was six months pregnant, Una danced and sang her heart out with the rest of the girls, only taking a brief break for one number each evening.

'All Fired Up! Live' began in Bournemouth on 2nd December 2011, playing to packed stadiums across the UK. Delighted fans rocked along to giant video projections, classic dance routines and catchy mash-ups of their favourite hits. There ain't no party like a Saturdays party!

Costume style – office secretary

Costume style – red, black, pink coloured leotards

Fired Up Tour

Costume style – silver dresses

Costume style – multi-coloured hood dresses

Costume style – Santa capes

Top Tour Memories

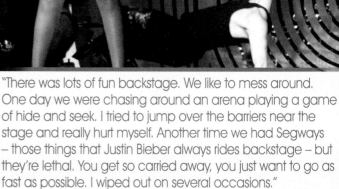

"We still have our pre-show ritual where we all high-five each other. Rochelle and I also have our own special one, too. Before we do a show we have to bang our hands together five times and say 'let's do this thing!'. I've no idea where that came from but we always do it."
Mollie

"I was six months pregnant, but I was really lucky and had no complications at all. In fact I had a burst of energy, so I was able to throw myself into the whole show every night. I did everything the other girls did – there was just one routine I didn't do as the moves were a bit risqué and I didn't think it was appropriate for me to be doing that while pregnant."
Una

"On tour everything's still the same – we can do arenas now, but apart from that, we're still just like five kids. I love it! The further North we go, the audiences have such fun and seem to get louder and louder. I particularly love going to Liverpool as I have family that way."
Rochelle

"I had a craving for chocolate and so I ate a lot of it during the tour. I'd have a couple of squares mid-show. The Saturdays are all over the catering, whenever we perform. It's always the first thing we ask – 'where's the food?' This time there was definitely more chocolate than normal."
Una

"There was lots of fun backstage. We like to mess around. One day we were chasing around an arena playing a game of hide and seek. I tried to jump over the barriers near the stage and really hurt myself. Another time we had Segways – those things that Justin Bieber always rides backstage – but they're lethal. You get so carried away, you just want to go as fast as possible. I wiped out on several occasions."
Vanessa

"We often have very quick costume changes on tour. On our first night in Bournemouth, Rochelle didn't get changed in time. We all came out of the floor in our lifts, but although Rochelle's lift went up, it was empty – she wasn't in there. She turned up half way through the song. Her zip had broken or something! I couldn't stop giggling."
Mollie

"Dublin was a fun town, but during that show the dancers pranked us. They always come out dressed in costumes during 'Just Can't Get Enough' and we each of us have a set partner that we dance with – mine was a cowboy! That night, they decided to switch around and dance with someone new…without telling us! We were very confused!"
Vanessa

"If there's one memory I'll take away from the 'All Fired Up' tour, it would be trying to make it into that lift on time every night."
Rochelle

"The thing I'll always remember about 'All Fired Up Tour' is saying 'Good Evening Wembley!' – that was ridiculous! It was so good. The whole tour experience is such an amazing thing, we enjoy it so much. All we've ever wanted are to be performers, so getting a chance to do that every night is amazing."
Rochelle

"For this tour we changed our rider. We ask for salted popcorn, hummus and crudités, plus things like baby wipes. Una used to have an addiction to salt and vinegar chipsticks, but she overdid it and has gone off them. Somebody's also put stinky blue cheese on the list, but no-one's owning up to who put it there!"
Mollie

"The rider did get bumped on up this tour. There's still stuff like fruit and nuts on there, but now there's like loads of cheese and fresh salami, which just gets left and stinks out the room. I think our managers were responsible for putting that stuff on there."
Vanessa

"Our rider was funny this year. There was loads of popcorn on it, which was down to me. Mollie makes us put toothbrushes and face wipes on there. It's not because she's sensible – Rochelle's the sensible one – Mollie just loves a toothbrush!"
Frankie

"It wasn't a party tour, it was chilled. We hung out, looked after Una, went for meals and then the boyfriends would visit. They're always welcome – it's like a really big family."
Rochelle

"We had a great end of tour party – it was the latest I'd ever stayed up! We went to a lovely bar in Dublin and invited everyone involved in our tour, from the dancers to hair and make-up, and the crew. After the bar closed we all went back to our hotel. Mark our tour manager had somehow managed to get the biggest suite in the whole hotel, so we had a big all-night party. We felt like proper rockstars – except that we all put our PJs on because it was just so nice to get out of heels!"
Mollie

"Mollie and I used to talk to the crowd at the beginning of the show. I'd kick off and say 'Hello, Birmingham!' or whatever, and then Mollie was supposed to say, 'we're really happy to be here.' But every night there'd be a silence on stage because Mollie was just standing there doing her 'sexy face'. I always had to prompt her!"
Frankie

Sit Your SATS! Part 2: Lyrics Quiz

The Saturdays' music couldn't be any catchier! Hollering into a hairbrush, singing along with mates or rocking out at a party – the tunes sound amazing wherever you are. How well do you know the girls' anthems?

Fill in the missing lyrics from these Saturdays classics.

1. Track title: 'All Fired Up'
Lyrics: We make the party super naughty,
Super naughty, dancin' _ _ _ _ _ _ _ _

2. Track title: 'Ego'
Lyrics: You can make the call when you're ready,
I will _ _ _ _ _ _ _ _ _ _ to help you break the fall

3. Track title: 'Higher'
Lyrics: I'm gonna stay here on my own and turn up my telephone,
If nothing's gained, _ _ _ _ _ _ _ _ ` _ _ _

4. Track Title: 'Issues'
Lyrics: Every time that I walk out the door,
Tell myself '_ _ _ _ ' _ _ _ _ _ _ _ no more'

5. Track title: 'My Heart Takes Over'
Lyrics: And look me in the eye,
Promise I won't cry,
This is your _ _ _ _ _ _ _ _ _ _ _ _

6. Track title: 'Notorious'
Lyrics: I'm an outlaw, I'm the big boss,
I'm a _ _ _ _ _ _ _ _ _ on the dance floor,

7. Track title: 'Missing You'
Lyrics: There's a blind force letting it win,
And it's longing to _ _ _ _ _ _ _ _ _ _ _

1. Lyrics: Each day you're not here,
Feels like a thousand years,
Need a magician to make time disappear,
Song title: ....

2. Lyrics: I tend to get what I want to,
are you starting to see, to see?
I think you do, I think you do,
Song title: ....

3. Lyrics: You're like an angel and you
give me your love,
And I just can't seem to get enough oh,
Song title: ....

4. Lyrics: I'm ready to be in control and the
ground isn't good enough for me,
I know where to find what I want and
I'm gonna keep on,
Song title: ....

5. Lyrics: You think I'm crazy,
I'm not I'm your baby,
I promise I'll always be,
Song title: ....

6. Lyrics: Wish I could turn back the page,
Re-write my point of view,
Song title: ....

7. Lyrics: What's it gonna be, are you willingly
walking away from this?
What's it gonna take?
Can you really break this love?
Song title: ....

Just Can't Get Enough Of...

Frankie then:

Life began in earnest for Frankie when she auditioned for her local stage school at the tender age of nine! It's no surprise that she passed the audition with flying colours – Frankie is a natural performer. She says that earning her place at the stage school opened up "a whole new world of possibility". On that very first open day, she also met a girl that would have a huge influence on her future – Rochelle!

Frankie now:

Now that the Sats have been so successful, Frankie is thrilled to have four best friends to work with. Over the years, she has experienced some tough times, but the instant she steps on stage her face lights up. Her nan describes her as 'sunshine n' showers'.

On love and relationships:

"I can't wait to have a family and get married, I want to do it quite young, but I'm not in a particular rush. I'm still with Wayne. He's moved to play at Brighton from Manchester City, which is great because he gets to live at home with me now."

On being all grown up:

"It's weird watching everyone just all of a sudden grown up. A couple of years ago we wouldn't have thought all of these major personal milestones could happen. It's so mental and so different, but then really it's not! It all feels absolutely right. At Una's wedding I cried like a baby the whole day. It was the same with Rochelle, too.

Mollie on Frankie:

"She is the naughty Saturday. It's like we're sisters, we completely take the mickey out of each other all the time, but then at the end of the day we're always there for each other."

Vanessa on Frankie:

"She laughs a lot of the time."

Rochelle on Frankie:

"Frankie is the biggest flirt in town… she even flirts with me sometimes!"

Una on Frankie:

"When Frankie's in a good mood, she's in such a good mood. When she's not in a good mood she's very quiet."

Frankie on Frankie:

"Occasionally I wake up and think everything looks horrible and my hair isn't right. Every girl wakes up to one of those days every now and then, don't they?"

Frankie

Tweet All About It

The Saturdays are huge fans of Twitter, often using the networking service to reveal secrets about the band and announce exciting news. Vanessa, Rochelle, Una, Frankie and Mollie also find it an ace way to stay connected to their fans.

While the Sats follow 1,500 people, more than 2.7 million are following them! Together the gang have sent more than 19,000 tweets. Here are ten of the best...

'Vocal warm ups must look so strange to people that don't know what the hell I'm doing LOL.'
Rochelle

'In the last 24hrs I have a) felt an earth tremor, & b) swam down a gorge! Just the normal Monday, no biggie! Lots of love, ur intrepid Saturday.'
Mollie

'Sometimes I wish I was a baby! it looks so comfy with all the music and lights and toys to soothe you off to sleep :) x'
Una

'Must. Stop. Eating. Haribo and chocolate fingers!!!! But I caaaaan't!!!!'
Frankie

'Sooo...LOLCANO...were just tryna think of some more..we have come up with spag lol so far lol any more?'
Vanessa

'As far as I'm concerned if u don't have cheap cheese at a BBQ, u may as well not have one. Lol. Allll about the cheap cheese!'
Frankie

'WOW chattiest cab driver EVER!!! Is it bad that he's just asked my occupation and I've said a marine biologist working with dolphins? :-)'
Mollie

'Meeting David Cameron yesterday for the 2nd time in a week :) check me ha!'
Rochelle

'OMG i was so tired after our 22hr shoot last night i didn't even notice my apartment's been PAINTED!!! Only just noticed this morning!! HA x'
-Mollie

'Our fans are literally the best! So much lovage for #teamsats Happy Friday to you all xx.'
Vanessa

Key in the Sats' handles and keep up with the band on Twitter.

Frankie: @FrankieTheSats
Rochelle: @RochelleTheSats
Una: @UnaTheSats
Vanessa: @VanessaTheSats
Mollie: @MollieTheSats

Sats Style – Rocking The

The red carpet can be a scary place for even the most experienced celebrity. With hundreds of cameras trained on your every move, it's no sitch to be wearing the wrong outfit. Fortunately The Saturdays are total naturals! Let's take a look at some of the girls' red carpet classics.

Fierce fashionistas

The girls have been wowing the fashion press ever since they first burst on the scene. At the Valentine's Day London première in 2010 they did it with white, feathered mini-dresses (Una and Frankie), black short print dresses (Mollie and Vanessa) and Rochelle's amazing red drape gown.

Hair, handbags & heels

They may have been at the 2011 GQ Men Of The Year Awards, but with these five fresh and fun looks, the band ensured the night was all about the girls!

Animal magic

Vanessa unleashes the animal in herself in this gorgeous giraffe print maxi dress at the launch of designer Roberto Cavalli's new London store in 2011. Add a Chanel handbag to her look and it's easy to see why the fashion mags were raving about her the next day

Keeping it simple

Una oozed style at the world première for The *Inbetweeners* in 2011. Her black and gold sparkly mini-dress, ankle boots and clutch bag showcased her effortless sense of cool!

Red Carpet

Nude, not neutral

So many stars have partied at London's Grosvenor Hotel, it can be hard to get noticed. In 2009, Rochelle had no trouble at all when she arrived in this gorgeous, strapless ivory ball gown.

Happy strappy

Who can claim to be more at home on the red carpet than our Mollie? Her dark chocolate, flared mini dress was bang on-trend at the *Marie Claire* Runway launch in London in 2012.

Making shapes

It's easy to see why Frankie is a regular in the best-dressed lists! At the 2010 Sony Radio Awards her cream wrap mini-dress scored yet another style hit. Frankie gave the look an edge with open-toed gladiator boots.

Grecian and gorgeous

The girls coordinated their looks for their appearance at the 2011 Capital FM Jingle Bell Ball. Each wore sparkly gold and white, with their own distinctive twist – Una in full-on gold, Frankie in a white mini-dress with gold chain detail, Ness in a gold lamé skirt and white blouse, Mollie in a sparkly gold top with a gorgeous Chanel skirt and Rochelle in an amazing white fringed dress!

Mollie shares her favourite day ever in The Saturdays...

"My favourite day would have to be the day we performed at Wembley Arena on the All Fired Up Tour. It was something I'd dreamt of doing since I was six years old! To come out on stage and see the stadium full and every seat taken was just incredible. It was quite a stressful day before that show because so many friends and family were coming. Our hometown shows are always the most nerve-wracking. I was really focused during sound check to make sure everything sounded perfect. That's me all over – I am a real worrier and I overthink everything. I drive myself mad because I can't switch off and when we're rehearsing, I lie there and go over and over the steps in my head. I'll even get out of bed and stand in front of the mirror and say 'right Mollie, you're not going to sleep until you've got these moves down!'"

My five fave moments...

"Receiving my birthday book from all of our Team Sats meant so much to me."

"Performing on So You Think You Can Dance? with the elevator opening. Incredible!"

Filming the 'Notorious' video in LA. I just felt really showbiz for one day!"

"When Cheryl and Kimberley came into our dressing room on our opening night on tour at Belfast. I was so star struck. It was just amazing."

"The day that we were told that we were in the band was just the best day ever."

My Favourite Day In The

Una shares her favourite day ever in The Saturdays...

"My favourite day ever has to be earlier this year, when we did a show in my home town, Thurles, in County Tipperary where I grew up. In the days before, I appeared on one of Ireland's most popular TV chat shows, The Late Late Show. On the programme I talked about the concert, but I didn't expect the reaction it would get.

On the day there were 5,000 people in the audience at the concert. The population of Thurles is only around 7,000 people, so that meant that practically the whole town had turned out to watch us! I never, ever thought I'd see the day where I'd be performing at that level for my local town. I felt so proud. While we were there I also shot a flip video for our website, showing fans all around the place. I even bumped into Mrs Persil, a teacher who taught me when I was nine years old. Although we are UK based, I'm Irish and I love it when we go back because I get to see all my family and my friends who still live over there."

My five fave moments...

"Winning a Glamour Award. Rochelle got to meet Kim Kardashian!"

"Filming the video for 'Higher' in LA was such a fun time in our lives. The sun was out and it was all chilled out and brilliant."

"Recording 'Last Call' with Lucie Silvas – one of my favourite singer-song writers in the world. It was a dream."

"Performing at the O2 in Ireland on the last date of our 'All Fired Up' tour, just before Christmas."

"The day after Aoife was born all the girls came together. It was like she was the sixth Saturday and all the Saturdays were together!"

Rochelle shares her favourite day ever in The Saturdays...

"My favourite ever day in the band would have to be when we signed our record deal, right at the start. It was such an amazing moment because there had been such a lot of talk and meetings but finally there we were, in the offices of our record company, with glasses of champagne, actually putting pen to paper. You do physically sign your name on a dotted line so that was a really big day.

When you start out and are picked from the auditions, you hope you're going to end up with a deal, but you never really know if it will work out. Even when we signed I didn't really know if we'd make it, but when we started performing gigs together I knew we'd be big. We just worked as a group.

After the signing the five of us went out to celebrate together but we didn't go clubbing or anything, we just went to Wagamama in Covent Garden – it doesn't sound very 'showbiz' but at the time it was one of our favourite places to eat. It's a bit different now, we couldn't all just pile into a restaurant in central London."

My five fave moments...

"Shooting the video for '30 Days'. It was such a fun day, being in a diner, eating lots of burgers and chips!"

"Supporting Take That on tour."

"Buying my first car. When we got signed I told my mum I was going to buy myself a Mini Cooper. In the end I went for a cream VW Beetle convertible. I fell in love with it."

"Auditioning our dancers for the tour."

"I loved the day that we filmed 'Missing You! It was so sunny and everyone was partying and it was great."

Vanessa shares her favourite day ever in The Saturdays...

"The standout day for me has to be when we did the London 'All Fired Up' show at Wembley Arena. I know all of the girls will say the same, but it really was amazing!

We were all so nervous as the show was the culmination of a tremendous amount of hard work. There were also so many people that are dear to us in the audience. I couldn't believe that we were going to be playing such a huge, iconic venue! I'll never forget coming up in the lifts, singing the first notes of 'Notorious'. We were dressed as secretaries, just like we are in the music video. To come up and see thousands of fans filling Wembley Arena was incredible.

To be honest, the whole tour was brilliant – it was so much bigger than the last one. This time we had all the dancers and our live band and sooooo many costume changes! We all struggled with those a bit, but the whole experience was unforgettable."

My five fave moments...

"I loved filming the 'Ego' video because we got to play all these different characters."

"Playing at G-A-Y, especially when we did our G-A-Y signing and we arrived on motorbikes."

"Learning the dance steps to 'All Fired Up', it's my favourite dance routine."

"I enjoyed recording 'Chasing Lights'. I just remember that day so perfectly."

"Playing T In The Park. It was such an amazing festival and there were thousands and thousands of people."

Frankie shares her favourite day ever in The Saturdays…

"My fave day ever in The Sats was when we met baby Aoife for the first time, the day after she was born. It was the most amazing, surreal moment. I couldn't believe Una was a mum, but there she was, looking gorgeous with this beautiful baby. Aoife was just so cute, with big kissable cheeks. It was an unforgettable experience and a huge high – very different from doing a show, but I loved it because it was just the five of us, as best friends, rather than a band.

From a professional point of view my best day was probably when we shot the video for our official single for Comic Relief, 'Just Can't Get Enough'. It was such a big deal for us. We felt so honoured to have been asked and it was great to be able to do something we do all the time, but this time, to help others. It was a really fun video to make, the atmosphere on set was so calm compared to most of our videos – things can get a bit stressful when there are tight schedules. This one was just so laid back and easy. It was filmed in a studio in London and we were dressed as pin-up girls.

My favourite moment on set happened when I was eating popcorn. Without warning all the crew pelted me with the stuff! They threw loads – it was so funny that the shot made it into the final video."

My five fave moments…

"The first day of the 'All Fired Up' tour when we were up in a lift behind the curtains and we could see all the crowd in front of us. It was just an amazing feeling."

"When we supported Girls Aloud it was such an exciting time for us and it was just the beginning. It was something we'll always remember."

"Getting give the plaque for two million record sales."

"Doing V Festival was amazing, especially the one in Chelmsford because all my friends and family were there. It's a just great feeling to know that pop is at the festivals!"

"Being asked to do the Poppy Appeal was amazing. We got to perform to all the soldiers and you know I love a soldier!"

Saturdays Sounds

The Sats are huge music fans! The fivesome's voices gel perfectly to make the amazing sound of the band, but what they listen to on their own headphones couldn't be more different.
Sneak a peek at the girls' playlists.

Una

Sheryl Crow
If It Makes You Happy

Norah Jones
Don't Know Why

Shania Twain
You're Still The One

KT Tunstall
Black Horse And The Cherry Tree

Damien Rice
Cannonball

Massive Attack
Unfinished Sympathy

Air
All I Need

The Prodigy
Breathe

Oasis
Don't Look Back In Anger

Linkin Park
Numb

Mollie

Britney Spears
Gimme More

Regina Spektor
Samson

Paolo Nutini
Last Request

Justin Timberlake
Cry Me A River

Michael Jackson
Man In The Mirror

Avril Lavigne
Girlfriend

Jimmy Eat World
The Middle

Timbaland
The Way I Are

Newton Faulkner
Dream Catch Me

Nelly Furtado
Big Hoops

Vanessa

Black Eyed Peas
I Gotta Feeling

Pussycat Dolls
Buttons

Gym Class Heroes
Cupid's Chokehold

Girls Aloud
Can't Speak French

Michael Jackson
Thriller

Jessie J
Domino

Master Shortie
Swagger Chick

Beyoncé
Single Ladies

Alicia Keys
Fallin'

Gwen Stefani
Luxurious

Dream collaborations

The girls have got a stack of music idols, but which artists do they dream of working with? The Sats spill the beans!

"I would love to team up with Take That. I'd love to actually do a performance with them where we were all on stage together. And of course it would be amazing to work with Britney – she's my idol. If I ever met her I'd keel over."
Mollie

"I'd love to collaborate with Beyoncé. I love her."
Rochelle

"In America we recorded with a team of writer/producers called The Jam – they're amazing. Literally every song they played us we loved. I'd like to work with them again."
Frankie

"It'd be cool to collaborate with Will.i.am. I love dance music. 'All Fired Up' is my fave track so I'd love to do something with David Guetta. Rihanna loves to collaborate – it would be cool to do something with her."
Una

Fill in your own playlist

My Playlist

A B C D E F G H I J K L M N O P Q R S T U V W X Y Z

Frankie

aramore
en It Rains

ter Shikari
ry You're Not A Winner

ty and Colour
e Your Scissors

e Shins
ple Song

e Bronx
rt Attack American

gs of Leon
Somebody

gen Heap
And Seek

y Winehouse
ie

ndie
Me

Benatar
breaker

A B C D E F G H I J K L M N O P Q R S T U V W X Y Z

Rochelle

Rihanna
Only Girl (In The World)

Chris Brown
Beautiful People

Ne-Yo
Beautiful Monster

Justin Timberlake
Sexy Back

Amy Winehouse
Back To Black

Usher
Yeah!

Mariah Carey
Honey

Taio Cruz
Dynamite

JLS
She Makes Me Wanna

Cheryl Cole
Call My Name

A B C D E F G H I J K L M N O P Q R S T U V W X Y Z

Looking Good!

The Sats are total fashionistas, but they're also firm believers that the best accessory is a sweet smile! Read some of the girls' beauty secrets, then find out how they like to work out.

Hair and make-up

Mollie:
I swear by Carita products and I like Estée Lauder illuminating concealer for under my eyes. I use Decléor moisturizer and have a Mac face and body foundation which is really light so you can use it for leg make-our make-up artist always uses a brilliant primer on my face to stop it looking shiny.

I'm useless at styling my hair, but I use Babyliss curling tongs. Our stylist Nick rough blow dries it and gives the top some extra attention. And because I have very soft baby hair he has to use tons of hairspray to hold it in place.

Vanessa:
My skin regime has gone downhill, I used to be really strict about it and cleanse tone and moisturise every day. Now I'm more of a soap and water girl.

I've changed my hair, it's highlighted and light brown – I am enjoying that. I'm hoping to leave it like this. I get bored very easily, but I'm liking this look!

Rochelle:
I'm always frightened that if I start using different products I'll have a breakout, so I just stick to the same old ones. My basic kit involves mascara, foundation and cream blushers.

I told myself that I'd also have regular treatments in the run up to the wedding but it's hard to fit them in when you're manic. From time to time I book a massage so I can relax, but I end up just lying there thinking about what I've got to do!

Una:
Luckily when we're working we have Nick and Celena to do our hair and make-up. But when you have a baby, vanity goes out the window. I look at my nails and think 'oh my gosh!' Rochelle always has amazing nails – she is most manicured person you'll ever meet. I get no time to even brush my hair any more. I just about manage to wash my face and moisturize.

For my wedding, my sister got me a lovely beauty gift – it was my 'something blue – a face cream called Guerlain Midnight Secret. It costs a lot and isn't something I would usually splash out on, but it's amazing. It's a late night recovery treatment. It makes you look as if you've had eight hours sleep even if you've only had two.

When I was pregnant, my hair was fabulous. I don't wash my hair every day and when I do, I put Moroccan oil on the ends to stop them getting dry.

Frankie:
When I'm not working, I can't be bothered to put a full face of make-up on. I feel OK as long as I have concealer to cover up any spots, bronzer for a bit of colour and some lip balm. It's my minimalist make-up kit.

My hair is still the same lopsided bob. I keep trying to think of different dos but so far no other style has grabbed me. I don't use conditioner on my hair because it's shiny anyway and if it's coated with too much product, it doesn't do what I want it to do.

The Saturdays Way

Body beautiful

Frankie:
Every year I say I'll buy a bike, but I don't. I am doing a lot of Pilates though! I love Pilates – it's not boring like the gym. I really enjoy the classes. The exercises are hard work, but Pilates makes you leaner and gives good muscle tone.

Rochelle:
In the first month after being engaged, I told myself I needed to really shape up, so I got myself a personal trainer and went running. It didn't last! I don't like that sort of exercise so I always just rely on the dancing we do.

I have started horse riding though. I'm OK at it – I used to ride when I was a kid. For my hen celebrations, my best friends surprised me with a riding lesson. It really made me want to get back in the saddle again! I can't jump or anything, but I'm loving it. In 2013 I'd like to do more of that.

Una:
Now I've had Aoife, I'm back doing everything the girls are doing – the dance routines and everything. I also go out and walk everywhere with the baby. I'm always up and about, burning anything I eat up with my natural energy. I love to be busy so that helps.

I want to take up swimming in 2013 and I'll take Aoife along. It's a nice thing for babies to do.

Mollie:
I go to the gym but I've also just bought a bike. Earlier this summer Frankie and I hired Boris bikes, rode around Hyde Park and bought ice creams. It was such fun that it inspired me to go out and get a bike of my own. I've wanted one for ages so I bought a classic, hybrid, touring bike good for shooting around. I live between Putney and Wimbledon so I like riding around the common and into the village. My mum's very strict with me so she reminds me to wear the geeky helmet and she also won't let me put Alfie in the basket. I have sat him there a couple of times though, just to see how he looks!

Vanessa:
I've had a bit of a break and I haven't done anything for the past month, but usually I have a personal trainer and I run uphill for 30mins and then do toning exercises for an hour and a half, a couple of times a week.. I can't do it on my own – I need someone to push me. I do it in my trainer's house in the garden so I'm not papped looking hideously pink and sweaty. It's difficult to look good running up a hill!

I am also really into Bikram yoga. It's the one where you do the moves in a really, really hot room. I love it and go every Sunday.

The Saturdays' videos sizzle! With some of the world's top directors lining up to work with them, each new release offers something fresh and exciting to surprise us all over again.

How many classic videos have you bopped along to? The song titles and video reels have got jumbled up on these pages. Read the descriptions, then draw a line to match each one up to the right tune.

The vids

1. Uh oh, the band have accidentally walked into a speed-dating night at a local diner. Undeterred, they join in!

2. Head-to-toe in black and dressed to kill the girls share their dance routine duties with a crew of latex covered dancers who are throwing shapes in a puddle!

3. A clever video within a video idea, we get to see what goes on when The Saturdays make a music clip, before going backstage at one of the gigs.

4. In a reflective mood, the girls head to a beach house for a chill. Whilst there, they spend some time looking out of the windows before going for an evening stroll to a bonfire.

5. A lucky fan stumbles across the band – complete with wind machines, male dancers and fireworks galore – rehearsing in an old factory and is treated to her own private gig!

6. Look out lads, The Saturdays aren't what they seem! The girls have acquired super powers and use them to get their own back on a fame hungry guy!

7. The girls are on holiday. Before meeting up for a dance on the beach, Frankie sits in a tree, Mollie rides a bike down a dusty road, Vanessa hangs out at a crumbling building, Una goes for a spin in the car and Rochelle paddles in the sea.

8. The band are in New York soaking up the sights and sounds of inner city life. Soon their enjoyment leads to a dance routine that peaks with the band throwing handfuls of glitter while standing on car bonnets!

9. In no way dressed for the weather or conditions (but looking awesome!), the girls wander around the desolate but beautiful Icelandic countryside.

10. The band prove that keeping it simple can often lead to the best results with a video that shows them dancing in colourful tights.

11. The Saturdays go for fun and flirty '40s glamour in this reinvention of a Depeche Mode release. Unsurprisingly it was a huge hit with the male fans!

12. On the top floor of an office block, the Sats play bored temps. When they take the lift downstairs, they become fun-loving party girls!

13. The band feel blue as they each remember failed relationships. Don't worry though, the girls soon get together and remember that they always have the band. Bring on the dancing!

The tunes

A. 'If This Is Love'

B. 'Up'

C. 'Issues'

D. 'Just Can't Get Enough'

E. 'Work'

F. 'Forever Is Over'

G. 'Ego'

H. 'Missing You'

I. 'Higher'

J. 'Notorious'

K. 'All Fired Up'

L. 'My Heart Takes Over'

M. '30 Days'

Just Can't Get Enough Of...

Una then:

Although she started life as quite a shy and small child, it didn't take young Una long to blossom! Performing wasn't her natural first step however – her story began in the swimming pool. After starting lessons at nine, she went on to become the fastest swimmer in Ireland. "I swam 50 metres in 37 seconds," she explains. "I'm very proud of that!" Within months, the shy, fussy-eating Una was just a memory. She hasn't looked back since!

Una now:

As well as being the Saturday's country-rock heart, Una proves that hard work and dedication really does pay off. Gigging in pubs with her guitar may be just a memory now, but she'll never forget the path that led her to pop success.

On love and relationships:

"Ben is always touring or training with England, so I cherish time with him. We're a proper family now. We don't do much when we have time off. We go out for food, and bring the baby. Sometimes we go to the local pub, but we're equally happy at home. Ben likes to drink cups of tea and eat biscuits. He likes watching TV shows like *Game Of Thrones* and *Spartacus*, as well as the horse racing. It's so boring, but he's really into checking the horses' form. So if the baby's sleeping, I do online shopping while he's doing that!"

On being all grown up:

It's great that Rochelle and I are at similar life stages –we got engaged within two weeks of each other. We've been a big support to each other.

On the morning of my wedding I was so laid back, there was no panic or stress. The stressful part is the build up. When the day comes you should actually relax and enjoy it – it's the best day of your life. I tried to pass that advice on to Rochelle. The girls were with me all morning. One of my favourite memories of the day was when I looked back as I was walking down the aisle. The girls were all crying happy tears – it was really special."

Vanessa on Una:

"What you see is what you get with Una."

Rochelle on Una:

"I genuinely feel that Una is my big sister."

Mollie on Una:

"Una's a really passionate person and I think it's amazing to have that in the band. She knows exactly what she wants and she goes for it."

Frankie on Una:

"She's very musical. She loves to play her guitar. She loves to write songs."

Pet Pals

The Saturdays girls are all potty about their pets! Every one of them dotes after at least one pup that is fluffy, affectionate and utterly adorable! Between them, the girl group has a pack of doggies to feed and take for walkies. The girls even managed to perform with animals for their 'Just Can't Get Enough' video for Comic Relief. Mollie cuddles a dog on a leopard print rug, while Frankie appears on a bike with a fluffball peeping out of her basket!

Rochelle is very proud of her Yorkshire terrier, Tiger, while Mollie coos over a tiny chestnut poodle called Alfie. Soon after Una and her fiancé Ben moved into their first place together, they got Jackson – a cute canine who's half pug, half jack Russell. Jackson seemed a bit lonely when they left him indoors and so it wasn't long before Una and Ben decided to get him a friend. Bono is a pug-Pomeranian cross with gorgeous rolls of sandy-coloured fur.

It didn't take long for Jackson to bond with his new puppy pal. "They are as thick as thieves now, really good friends," said Una. "They're always playing and making noises and nibbling each other and play-fighting."

Frankie is famous for her devotion for the two little people in her life – her pug Presley and pint-sized Chihuahua Pixie. Vanessa's retinue includes a much-loved poodle called George and Pomeranian cross Peaches. George and Peaches live at Nessa's mum and dad's house, but she also shares Maggie, an adorable Puggle, with her boyfriend.

Although most of their pups are small enough to fit into their handbag, the Sats are very serious about looking after them. In September 2011, the girls jumped at the chance of backing a new campaign to stop people treating pets like fashion accessories. The band teamed up with Nintendo and the Dog's Trust to remind people that dogs are not toys. "Dogs are living animals," said Mollie. "We see ours as members of the family. We take it very seriously and you have to realize that when you have a dog it is a huge responsibility. But with that responsibility comes a best friend forever."

American Dreams

Now that they're the queens of the UK charts, what will the Saturdays do next? In 2013 the girls are setting their sights on the biggest pop nation of them all – the USA! Here's an exclusive preview of Team Sats' American dreams...

"English music is doing so well at the moment, it's hard for girl bands to make it in the US – there aren't any at the moment. I think that they'll hopefully like us because we're very British, we have real unity, we get on and everyone sings.

I love LA. We haven't spent much time over there yet but when we do, we shop constantly. We all go shopping together and everyone breaks off to have a look around. It can be long-winded, but we have to stick together really because no one really chooses anything without someone else looking at it first. My favourite shop over there is Victoria's Secret. We love buying undies there. You can't get any of it here although they are opening a shop in London soon. It's a shame really – sometimes it's nice to have a few things that you can't get in the UK."

Frankie

"I'm so passionate and driven to make it in the States. It's an exciting time for British pop. One Direction are so adorable, as are The Wanted. They're doing so well in the US, and Olly Murs has been there too. All the British acts are doing brilliantly.

There are some great places in LA. On our last trip, we have dinner in a really lovely restaurant called Katana with Flo Rida. It was lovely to see him again, he's so laidback and down to earth, but then he lives a superstar lifestyle and is really into bling!

You can run into famous people in LA. We thought we saw Angelina Jolie in her car last time! We're not household names over there so it's only when we're all together that we get recognized right now."

Mollie

"We always say that world domination is our thing! I don't know why Americans are so into British pop, but whatever it is, we're going to run with it. I think Americans and Brits complement each other – we appreciate the differences. They like our humour and they like our music in the same way that we love their music.

LA is the only place outside the UK where I feel I know where I'm going. We've been there a lot and I do feel at home. I like to go to Melrose Avenue and Rodeo Drive. There are so many streets full of amazing shops – they have great shops for nice tees and jeans.

Rochelle

"In the US it will be like starting again, which is both daunting and exciting. We have social media on our side though. With our website and sites like YouTube and Twitter people can research us and check out our back catalogue – there's so much people can tap into already, which is good.

Una

"We're going to be in LA a lot more in 2013. American audiences love Adele – she really set the Brit thing off for everyone, opening doors that were previously closed. There are a few boy bands in the US, but there aren't any girl groups. There's a gap in the market!

Vanessa

Sit Your SATS! Part 4: Fan Challenge

Keeping track of The Saturdays is a full-time job, but their fans are totally devoted to supporting the fab five everywhere they go. Are you a dedicated Sats-o-holic? Sit this fan challenge and find out how many facts and figures you've learned about the girls. Grab a pen and have fun – it's all about the random details!

True or false?
Are the following Sats statements total rubbish or the real deal?

1. Frankie is a US TV addict, her current favourite show is One Tree Hill.
☐ True ☐ False

2. Mollie is a demon skier and in the past once represented Great Britain.
☐ True ☐ False

3. Vanessa is a whiz with a wok and is planning her own cookery show.
☐ True ☐ False

4. Rochelle has a famous uncle, former England footballer Paul Ince.
☐ True ☐ False

5. Before finding fame Una ran a chain of successful sports shops.
☐ True ☐ False

6. Mollie's favourite saying is 'Check this bad boy out!'.
☐ True ☐ False

7. Vanessa loves to travel and thinks the Philippines is the best place she's visited.
☐ True ☐ False

8. Frankie's most-prized possession is a signed picture of Terry Wogan.
☐ True ☐ False

9. When she was younger, Una chose 'Imogene' as her confirmation name.
☐ True ☐ False

10. If a pop career hadn't worked out, Rochelle would have liked to have been a lab technician.
☐ True ☐ False

True or false?
Connect the band member to the correct and utterly random fact!

1. This Saturday girl claims that she doesn't like certain foods before she's even tried them!

2. Want to impress this band member? Take her for breakfast, it's her favourite thing to do!

3. This Saturday has been known to wake up neighbours with her singing.

4. For her first stage appearance at school, this band member played a character called Little Miss Mouse, who lived in a bin!

5. This girl dreams of bringing out an amazing foundation that matches every skin tone.

Sats Style – Girls About Town

We've seen what the girls wear when they're performing and attending exclusive red carpet events, but what about a night on the town? The Sats love getting all dressed up and partying with their pals! Check out some of their favourite fashion hits.

Mar-V-ellous!

Ness chose a classy sequin frock for Rochelle and Marvin's joint birthday party in 2011. The central V was both eye-catching and super-flattering.

Playing it down

Rochelle and Frankie played it cool when they met funnyman David Walliams at Naomi Campbell's Fashion For Relief event in 2010. Their laid back jackets proved that both girls sparkle with or without sequins!

Animal print edgy

Vanessa went for a rock look when she attended The Muppets première. Her combination of a leather biker jacket with an animal print dress even won her a kiss from Kermit!

Disney

70

Print perfect

Una used clever coordinating to pull off a busy print for this night out in London in May 2012. By matching her shoes, belt and bag, she gave her funky mini-dress room to shine!

City chic

Frankie and Mollie kept it colourful and cool when they headed out for a night at the clubs in London. Jeans, a peach vest and turquoise jacket gave Mollie some dressed down style while Frankie's black playsuit and bright yellow suit jacket let her show off her tanned legs!

Glamming it up

Una and Rochelle opted for mini-dresses when they attended the Pride Of Britain Awards in 2011. Rochelle went for a chic midnight blue look while Una picked a stylish one shoulder LBD. What's your favourite? We can't pick!

Belt up!

After recording her appearance on The Late Show in 2011, Mollie hit the tiles in Dublin. Her buttoned down dress and over-sized suit jacket were cleverly cinched in with a brown leather belt.

Surprising Saturdays!

A quick check of the girls' Twitter accounts will tell you that The Saturdays' world is full of crazy, random things! Whether it's strange habits, unusual fears or weird skills, the girls have them in abundance! Here are some facts about the band that you probably didn't know…

Forget real dangerous things like sharks or spiders, Frankie has an out-of-control phobia of tomato ketchup!

Mollie never goes anywhere with having her trusty video camera in her bag.

This year, Vanessa and Rochelle went to Abu Dhabi. The girls stayed in the hotel where they filmed Sex And The City 2. They claim it was just as amazing as it looked in the film. Now all the Sats want to go back with their boyfriends and husbands.

Frankie's most treasured item of clothing is a jumper she 'borrowed' from her dad that he had owned since his teens. The star wears it as a dress!

Mollie and Frankie like to have tour sleepovers, where they get in their PJ's and watch a movie together. The next morning they have a full English breakfast in bed.

Although they got married in July, Rochelle and Marvin's honeymoon isn't til Christmas because of the couple's hectic work schedule.

Vanessa has been into Hello Kitty since she was five years old. She used to have the duvet and now she has loads of statuettes. She'd love a Hello Kitty toaster, but her real ambition is to visit to the Hello Kitty Land theme park in Tokyo.

Mollie and Frankie see each other a lot. When they're at Mollie's place they order Indian, but at Frankie's they go for Thai. They're also both addicted to salted popcorn, although Frankie likes to put melting chunks of chocolate in hers. Ew!

Mollie has a spontaneous side. This Spring, she and a friend decided to go to Paris for 24 hours. They just booked Eurostar tickets two hours before going and jumped on a train.

Frankie has just started snowboarding.

Rochelle says her pet peeve is smelly people in the London underground.

One of Una's cousins ran for Ireland in the 2012 Olympic Games. His name is Paul Hessian and he entered the 100m and 200m sprint.

Key in the Sats' handles and keep up with the band on Twitter.

Frankie: @FrankieTheSats
Rochelle: @RochelleTheSats
Una: @UnaTheSats
Vanessa: @VanessaTheSats
Mollie: @MollieTheSats

Just Can't Get Enough Of...

Vanessa then:

Being a popstar isn't always glamorous. Behind the glitz there are early alarm calls, car journeys and late nights. Vanessa takes all this in her stride – she has been working hard her whole life! When she was little, she used to set off at 6am every Saturday to drive from her home in Somerset to the Sylvia Young Theatre School in London. After a year, her mum and dad finally moved the family closer. "I think they agreed to do it because I never stopped singing!" she recalls.

Vanessa now:

Vanessa has come a long way since her first West End break in The King and I. The other Sats adore her naughty humour, twinkly eyes and traffic-stopping singing voice!

On love and relationships:

"I've been with my boyfriend for about a year – it was secret for a while but now everyone knows. He's a stylist and he works with people like JLS, but he doesn't get involved in anything I wear and I would never ask him advice. I wouldn't buy him clothes as a present either, unless he gave me a hint!

We're lucky as all our boyfriends get on really well. A bit too well actually. They all text each other when we're going away and arrange boyfriend gatherings. It's a proper bromance!"

On being all grown up:

"I've matured a lot. When I started in the Saturdays I was only 17, so I've grown up. I live on my own now, too. I'm quite messy, but I'm not dirty so I keep my place clean and I do my own washing and stuff – I don't take it home to my mum! I'm really enjoying having my own space.

And now, of course, we've got a baby! I keep saying 'we' because it feels like Aoife's ours. I've loved meeting and getting to know Una's baby. I'm a little obsessed! She's the most beautiful little girl and has all this amazing hair. I've even fed her and burped her. It's good practice for the future, but I'm only 22 so I'm not ready for weddings and babies yet. Maybe when I'm 30!"

Una on Vanessa:

"Vanessa's our little baby."

Rochelle on Vanessa:

"She's honestly on a different planet! She has the dirtiest laugh ever!"

Frankie on Vanessa:

"Vanessa and I can be quite mischievous together. We get bored easily, especially when we're waiting around in the studio."

Vanessa on Vanessa:

"I'm a free spirit and I live in the moment."

Mollie on Vanessa:

"Whenever I'm up for a party, Vanessa's my girl!"

Vanessa

The Saturdays Super Grid

It's time to see if you're of 'Higher' intelligence when it comes to puzzles - or if you have 'Issues'. Check out the list of The Saturdays-related phrases and words on the opposite page. Now, see if you can locate them all within the grid on this page.

C	H	A	S	I	N	G	L	I	G	H	T	S	W	V
I	T	V	B	S	O	A	D	F	H	E	W	D	U	G
V	Y	A	K	X	T	T	P	A	A	A	C	O	H	I
W	E	A	O	C	O	U	K	M	O	L	L	I	E	F
O	Q	I	G	S	R	U	V	E	N	Y	J	K	A	T
R	X	F	S	T	I	N	A	Y	Y	R	Q	S	D	H
K	O	R	E	S	O	W	N	F	O	D	V	A	L	I
D	U	C	E	F	U	K	E	A	U	F	U	G	I	S
S	H	U	H	H	S	E	S	V	R	G	M	J	N	I
E	F	T	I	E	O	T	S	S	R	H	O	V	E	S
G	J	H	G	O	L	Y	A	F	A	J	F	D	S	L
V	G	D	H	H	T	L	T	J	D	S	S	O	O	O
D	W	E	E	F	S	J	E	P	A	S	H	P	G	V
R	E	W	R	E	S	K	D	F	R	A	N	K	I	E
M	I	S	S	I	N	G	Y	O	U	R	S	C	Q	A

Chasing Lights   Issues   Rochelle   Missing You

Notorious   On Your Radar   Work   Headlines

Healy   Ego   Vanessa   Higher

Mollie   If This Is Love   Frankie

DAYS

Saturday Sensations –

With the girls' videos constantly playing on the music channels, their music never out of the charts and pictures filling up magazines, barely a day goes by without a story, some gossip or a slice of celebrity hearsay about the band appearing in a newspaper or trending online. That doesn't mean that they're all true however! Over the years, there have been some incredible Saturdays rumours doing the rounds. Here are five of the best, completely debunked just for you!

Sssshhoe Princess.

The rumour: Having made what the press termed 'her first fashion faux pas', at a recent polo match, when her stiletto heels got wrecked in the boggy grass, Mollie is working quietly on designing a range of wedge heels for a high street store.

The reality: Although Mollie loves fashion and does blog about style for InStyle magazine, she has not yet made a move into fashion design. She continues to be a fan of heels, although will perhaps choose chunkier ones to her next country event.

Rumour rating: It's heely untrue!

Maternity mayhem!

The rumour: The band have decided to use Una's pregnancy and the birth of Aoife to catch up on some rest and all agreed to take two years off.

The reality: While some people assumed that one of the band becoming a mother might have derailed the Saturdays' plans, they hadn't banked on the girls' can-do, go-get-em attitude! While Una needed a short time away from the group, The Saturdays kept working hard. "They're a huge help to me because Aoife comes along a lot of the time, so they have no choice," Una explained. "I'll be like, 'oh ten minute break – here you go, change that nappy'."

"We've got tours to do, albums out, singles out, we've got a baby," Auntie Rochelle added. "We are all go at the minute. It's good to be like that. And it's nice we've got a good balance as well, that we can really fit our personal lives into it."

Rumour rating: A full-on fib!

Rumours and Reality

Strictly Rochelle?

The rumour: Rochelle will be appearing on the next series of hit BBC dance show Strictly Come Dancing.

The reality: Although Rochelle did flex her dancing muscles on the Strictly Come Dancing Special for Children in Need, back in 2010, she hasn't signed up for the series, preferring to concentrate on her commitments with The Saturdays. She does however, admit to practicing lifts at home in the living room with Marvin, having received praise from catty judge Craig Revel Horwood for her lifts during the American Smooth.

Rumour rating: A load of mambo jumbo!

Celebrity little sister?

The rumour: Keen to start making a name for herself outside of the band, Vanessa has agreed a deal to appear on the next series of Celebrity Big Brother!

The reality: Aside from the The Saturdays 24/7, Vanessa is the only Sat so far to dip her foot into another reality TV show after appearing in Popstar To Opera Star. But joining the housemates on CBB? Not likely.

Sources claimed Ness is set to join boxer Ricky Hatton, ex-Blue Peter presenter Andi Peters and Scottish television personality Carol Smillie inside the house. But while the Big Brother bosses keep the list of contestants a closely guarded secret, it is unsure whether Vanessa would do it even if offered.

Rumour rating: Telly tosh!

Frankie's flying the nest?

The rumour: After filming their video for 'Higher' in Los Angeles, Frankie fell in love with the city and has decided to up sticks and move there permanently.

The reality: In August 2009, the band jetted into the US to make a video for their single 'Higher'. Though it is indeed set in New York, the band filmed the video on a movie lot in Los Angeles. Frankie was completely taken with the city but despite the rumours, the admitted self-confessed homebody has no plans to leave London and move there... yet!

"I love Los Angeles – that's one of my favourite places to go. I've never been there for a proper holiday, but I've always thought that one day I'd like to live there," Frankie explained. "The shopping is amazing, there are great cities nearby, and I just really like the feel of the place."

Rumour rating: Fairly false. Although there is a small element truth there, Frankie's not leaving!

Which Saturday Are You?

Do you rock like Rochelle, are you fierce like Frankie or are you more of a Mollie? Now's your chance to find out exactly which member of the band you are closest to! Simply read the eight statements below and choose the ones you feel most apply to you. When you've finished, tot up the letters you ticked the most to reveal which Saturday you really are!

1. At school, I'm most likely to be found...
A - listening to what the teacher is saying and making notes.
B - chatting to friends and making sure they're OK.
C - making arrangements for this weekend's party!
D - talking to the boys!
E - having a heart to heart with my best friend.

2. My favourite way to spend a lazy Sunday morning is...
A - going out for brunch.
B - making breakfast in bed for my family.
C - sleeping in – it was hectic last night!
D - gossip on the phone with my mates.
E - trying out new make-up techniques.

3. If I fancy a night at the cinema, I am most likely to see...
A - a comedy.
B - a romantic movie.
C - a street dance film.
D - the hot new teen flick.
E - a Hollywood classic.

4. I've got five minutes to spare online, do I...
A - do a bit of homework research.
B - shop for cute and quirky presents for my pals.
C - check eBay for bargain party outfits.
D - log onto my Twitter account.
E - browse some designer stores.

5. I would never leave home without...
A - my lip balm.
B - my mobile phone.
C - an emergency pair of heels!
D - my make-up kit.
E - my purse.

6. I'm planning a girl's night in, me and my friends will be...
A - dressing up in crazy old clothes and having a laugh.
B - having a total pampering session.
C - singing karaoke baby!
D - sharing all the latest gossip.
E - chatting for hours and hours and h-o-u-r-s!

7. My pals would say I am...
A - a hilarious, a lovable dork!
B - always there when they need me.
C - ready to party, day or night.
D - the person to turn to when they want to be cheered up.
E - the best listener they know.

8. The phrase that is most likely to appear on my reports is...
A - 'she always tries her hardest'.
B - 'she loves looking after people'.
C - 'she has a playful personality'.
D - 'she's a very popular girl'.
E - 'she will do anything for her friends'.

How did you answer?

Mostly As
You are most like... Mollie
You always like to look your best, but your friends love the fact that you don't take yourself too seriously. Like Mollie, you're a good girl at heart, even though you sometimes try to be bad!

Mostly Bs
You are most like... Una
You're a mother figure to your mates, but no one should be fooled by the way you fuss about your girls – just like Una, you've got a naughty side too!

Mostly Cs
You are most like... Vanessa
Always looking for a good time, you can be relied upon to put some fun into everything you do. Just like Ness, you're the person your pals turn to when they want to party!

Mostly Ds
You are most like: Frankie
Funky, flirtatious and fun, you've always got your finger on the pulse of what's happening. You know all the best goss, just like lovable Frankie!

Mostly Es
You are most like... Rochelle
You have a taste for the finer things in life, but just like Rochelle you're equally happy just having a good chat! You're great at keeping secrets and giving advice.

Big Stars, Little Screen

Appearing on TV is as natural to the Sats as living and breathing. Over the years, the girls have starred in documentaries, appeared on talent shows and even made a cameo appearance in Hollyoaks!

In 2010 The Saturdays filmed a fly-on-the-wall series called The Saturdays: 24/7 for ITV2. A plucky camera crew followed the girls on tour, allowing the Sats to reveal what it was really like being inside the girl band of the moment. Fans were thrilled to see just how the close the five were – even though they are constantly together the Sats really are best friends!

After their success on 24/7, the group went on to star in a six part documentary for Channel 4 called The Saturdays: What Goes On Tour, Stays On Tour. Did you catch it? As well as giving us behind-the-scenes access to the band, viewers got to see how much hard work and long hours travelling goes into the job. When asked how she felt about being followed around by a cameraman day and night, Rochelle replied, "I feel sorry for the cameraman really!"

Keep tuned in – you never know when a Sats might pop up next! In 2010, the girls appeared in a spooky episode of Ghosthunting with Yvette Fielding; and Vanessa famously starred in reality comp Popstar To Opera Star. In 2012 Una was thrilled to announce that she had joined the judging panel of a brand new sport entertainment show on ITV1 called Let's Go Gold! Una will be sat alongside Rio Ferdinand, Freddie Flintoff and Martine McCutcheon, watching teams from across the UK put an entertainment spin on their fave sports.

Last year, Vanessa and Rochelle were filmed in Tanzania, Africa for Comic Relief, in a bid to help girls as young as 12 who are forced into marriage and having babies. Both band members talked to the girls about their life experiences. The trip was about educating young people and letting them know that they have choices.

So what next? The Sats recently revealed that they were going to take their unique blend of party pop to the USA.

Sats Style – Girls About Town

Everyone needs a little time off now and again, but the Sats always make sure their style is working it even when they're not! Flick through this style file to see how the girls keep it fresh and fabulous when they're dressed down and chilling. Playsuits and skinny jeans, biker jackets and flip flops – what's your fave relaxed look?

Shorts and simple

When the girls played at the V Festival in 2011 they got to enjoy some downtime too. Frankie headed out to see the sights dressed in a basic vest top and tailored khaki shorts. Classic and cool!

Easy and elegant

Fashion-lover Mollie jumped at the chance to attend London Fashion Week during some recent time off. In a simple navy blue playsuit, tan heels and matching bag she managed to keep it dressed down but still totally Saturdays!

Shopper sensation

Rochelle's skinny jeans, hard-to-find vintage blue biker jacket and striped top was the perfect outfit for a day at the shops with her boyfriend.

Sweet sweaters

Being a huge sports fan, Mollie jumped at the chance of attending the World ATP Tour tennis finals in 2011. While the players sweated it out on the court, Molls stayed cool in jeans and a simple V-neck jumper.

Flowery and fabulous

With a pair of jodhpurs, flat shoes, pretty, but baggy top (not forgetting a yet-to-be Aoife onboard), Una showed she had found a way to keep comfortable and still look great throughout her pregnancy.

Back to black

Fashionistas can't have enough black in their wardrobes! Ness showed of her perfect street style when she was snapped in London in 2011. The star opted for feet-friendly heels, skinny jeans, black vest and a low key hoodie.

Fashion pack

Celebrity pals Nicola Roberts and Rochelle caused confusion when they attended the KTZ fashion in 2012. With Nicola's oversized Cleopatra T-shirt and Rochelle satin twist on the classic overcoat, were they there to watch the fashion or join in!?

All wrapped up

Frankie was every bit the off-duty popstar when she picked up some coffee to go in 2010. With heels, skinny jeans, black leather jacket and Aviator shades, Frankie couldn't help turning heads wherever she went.

Holiday honey dreaming

Vanessa kept the holiday feeling going when she arrived back in the UK after a break in early 2011. With sandals, a maxi dress and denim jacket she not only looked cool – she could also be pool-ready in under a minute!

California dreaming

Una captured the relaxed Californian spirit perfectly when she went shopping in Los Angeles. In her flip flops, denim shorts and oversized shades she looked like she'd just wandered off the Hills!

No one could accuse the girls of having nothing to say for themselves, in fact the gang love nothing better than a good natter! Can you work out who said each of these quotes? Take the final SATS test and find out!

1. A Saturday said: "We do get excited when we're in the charts. Each morning I wake up to a message from Rochelle to say 'guess what, we're number whatever today!'"

Who said that? ....

2. A Saturday said: "They were all there, The Queen, all the Royal Family. It was such an incredible day. It was amazing. You get sent the gift list… and we bought them a top of the range bin – a really good one."

Who said that? ....

3. A Saturday said: "I keep thinking when I have kids they'll grow taller than me and I'll be like, 'off to your room' and they'll just look at me and walk past me!"

Who said that? ....

4. A Saturday said: "It's a completely different way of singing, I think I will just leave the opera where it is right now."

Who said that? ....

5. A Saturday said: "I picked a magazine and saw a feature about all the celebrity mums and how much maternity leave they gave themselves. It said Victoria Beckham took like two weeks, so that will probably be what it's like for me."

Who said that? ....

6. A Saturday said: "The most romantic thing that ever happened to me was a private dinner on a beach with a pianist and there were candles floating in the sea."

Who said that? ....

7. A Saturday said: "I come from a family of girls, I went to an all-girls school and I'm in a girl band, so I guess it's fitting that I'm having a daughter."

Who said that? ....

8. A Saturday said: "Ooooh I love One Direction, they're so adorable, they make such a great little boy band."
Who said that? ....

9. A Saturday said: "I don't really go that much to the big clubs where the paparazzi and the media will be, you know? I'm a local pub kind of girl who likes hanging out with my mates."

Who said that? ....

10. A Saturday said: "I'm happy to be curvy, I'm happy to be womanly and I think that comes from happiness in everything else in my life too. The last thing I worry about now is what I look like."

Who said that? ....

11. A Saturday said: "I always carry around Elizabeth Arden 8 hour cream, it's essential!"

Who said that? ....

12. A Saturday said: "I have to be honest at first I think we were all like 'oh my god this is weird.' I mean you don't wake up at five in the morning and expect a camera to be in your face when you've just got out of the shower."

Who said that? ....

13. A Saturday said: "I do have a good sense of smell! You smell quite shower fresh... I don't know why I sounded so shocked! You smell clean."

Who said that? ....

14. A Saturday said: "We don't want to be in people's faces, but we do want people to get to know our individual personalities. We've definitely got nothing to hide."

Who said that? ....

15. A Saturday said: "I'm one of those girls who in all honesty can appreciate how beautiful another girl is."

Who said that? ....

See You Next Saturday...

We know the girls are hard at work making a new album, but what else does the future have in store for the Sats? Here are The Saturdays' hopes for 2013 and beyond...

"We'll carry on writing and recording a new album and we want to go on tour again. We have a new single out at the beginning of the year too."

"Our new album is a work in progress. We're still going to be doing what we do best – making infectious pop music – but there will be some surprises in 2013. Our next single is definitely pop with a twist."

"We're going to be in LA a lot more. I think Adele's success has opened doors for everyone and there aren't any girl groups in the US, so hopefully they'll like us. And we've got a new single coming out which is really fun. It includes a surprising new collaboration, too."

"Finding out we're getting to go to America is a massive step for us as a group, we never thought it would happen for us so we're nervous, but excited. We don't know much about it yet, but we'll be out there for about three months. We'll all live together so that'll be fun."

"I'll be a mum and wife, but The Saturdays will carry on as ever. I didn't let my pregnancy slow me down – I shot a music video a week before I gave birth and was back in action after five weeks. What's happened this year has felt like a very natural progression. Now none of us can imagine life or the band without Aoife around. I love what I do so much and I want to work and provide for her. I can't wait!"

Before we go, we want to say thank you for your amazing support during the last year. We're sending a massive shout out to all the old fans who have been there from the start, plus the new fans who've discovered us more recently. With all your tweets and messages, we feel like we know many of you personally. You're as much a part of the band as we are.

Now we're entering a whole new chapter for The Saturdays and it's going to be mega! Watch this space – 2013 is sure to be the best year ever. We can't wait to share it with you.

Lots of love from The Sats

Answers

Pages 18-19

Sit Your SATS! Part 1: Tick Test

1. Mollie
2. 2007
3. Rochelle
4. swimmer
5. Vanessa
6. Glamour Awards
7. The Saturdays: 24/7
8. 'If This Is Love'
9. Aoife
10. Elizabeth
11. TV Presenting
12. Popstar To Opera Star
13. collaborate with the band
14. 'On Your Radar'
15. Girls Aloud

Pages 20-21

Saturday Girls Crossword

F	O	R	E	V	E	R	I	S	O	V	E	R
	O											I
	C											D
	H	E	A	D	L	I	N	E	S			E
	E											
A	L	L	F	I	R	E	D	U	P			
	L		L		A			P				
	E	G	O		D							
T		E			A							
C	A	N	T		F	R	A	N	K	I	E	U
K								I				N
E				V	A	N	E	S	S	A		
S								G				

Pages 38-39

Sit Your SATS! Part 2: Lyrics Quiz

Where are the words?

1. on the bar
2. not be there
3. Nothing's won
4. I can't take it
5. Choice to make
6. Gangster
7. Tear us apart

Name the tune

1. 30 Days
2. Work
3. Just Can't Get Enough
4. Up
5. If This Is Love
6. Forever Is Over
7. My Heart Takes Over

Pages 60-61

Sit Your SATS! Part 3: Video Links

1. M
2. K
3. A
4. C
5. E
6. G
7. H
8. I
9. L
10. B
11. D
12. J
13. F

Pages 68-69

Sit Your Sats! Part 4: Fan Challenge

True or false?

1. True
2. True
3. False
4. True
5. False
6. True
7. True
8. False
9. True
10. False

Random facts

1. Frankie
2. Mollie
3. Vanessa
4. Una
5. Rochelle

Pages 76-77

It's A Saturdays World Wordsearch

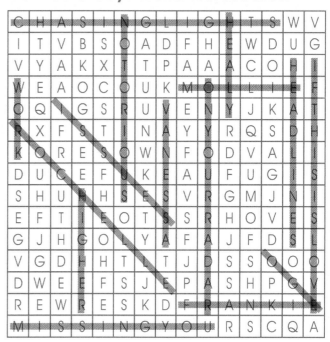

Pages 88-89

Sit Your SATS! Part 5: Who Said That?

1. Mollie
2. Una
3. Frankie
4. Vanessa
5. Una
6. Frankie
7. Una
8. Mollie
9. Vanessa
10. Rochelle
11. Mollie
12. Vanessa
13. Rochelle
14. Rochelle
15. Frankie